INSIDE THIS ANN

D0230281

I've hidden 8 'X' logos within this annual! Can you sniff 'em out?

£6.99

THE ORIGINS OF... WOLVERINE

EARLY YEARS!

Wolverine's incredible story begins over 100 years ago in Alberta, Canada. He was born James Howlett, the son of a rich family. As a child, James's best friends were a young girl called Rose and a boy called Dog, the son of the local groundskeeper Thomas Logan.

TRAGEDY STRIKES!

When James was in his mid-teens, Dog's father was fired. Furious at their expulsion from the manor, Logan and Dog returned to the Howlett estate intending to rob it.

However, during the burglary James attacked the groundskeeper in a berserk rage. As James struck, claws erupted from his knuckles and he fatally stabbed Logan. Terrified by what had happened, Rose and James fled the manor.

ON THE RUN!

Eventually, the two found refuge at a stone quarry in British Colombia. To protect his identity, James took the name Logan. But he was soon given another nickname by his fellow workers. They called him Wolverine, as he would work so hard in the quarry, he was like a wolverine digging for a root.

PAST CRIMES!

Their peaceful life was shattered when a now grown-up Dog tracked them down looking for revenge. Logan and Dog fought, but during the battle Rose was accidentally killed. Horrified, Logan fled into the nearby woods. Driven half mad by the loss of Rose, Wolverine became more like an animal than a man; running wild in the forests...

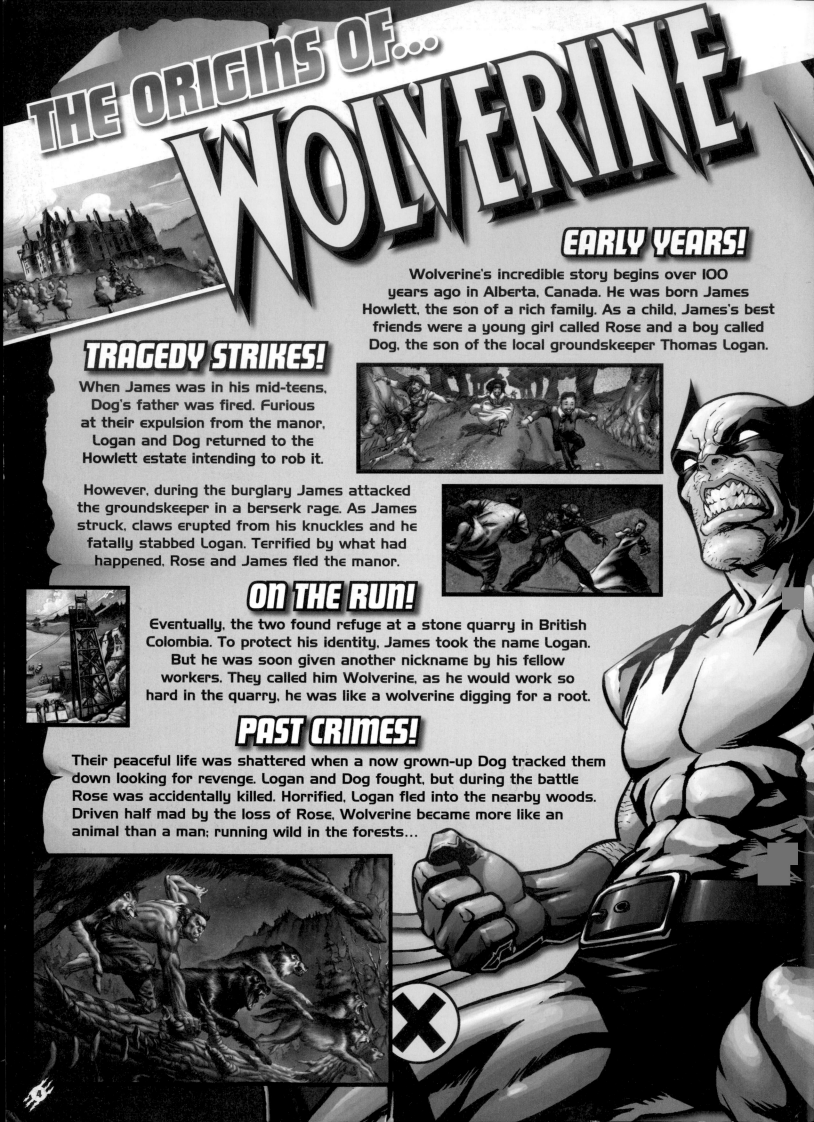

A LONE WARRIOR!

Eventually Wolverine returned to civilisation. He spent the next 60 years travelling the world, embarking upon numerous adventures. He fought in both world wars, worked as a secret agent and even trained to become a samurai in Japan.

WEAPON X

But his life changed forever when Weapon X, a covert military organisation who conducted illegal experiments on humans and mutants, kidnapped him.

In an effort to create the ultimate super soldier, the Weapon X scientists bonded the indestructible metal adamantium to Wolverine's bones and wiped his memory. But Wolverine proved too strong for the scientists to contain and he escaped the facility in an insane bestial state.

NEW BEGINNINGS!

Wolverine was found by a young couple called James and Heather Hudson, who nursed him back to health. James Hudson worked for the Canadian government and realised that Wolverine's amazing abilities would make him the perfect super powered secret agent. He offered Wolverine a job as a covert agent. Grateful for the support the couple had given him, Wolverine accepted James's offer.

TURN TO PAGE 30 TO DISCOVER THE NEXT CHAPTER IN WOLVERINE'S AMAZING LIFE...

Doctor Hudson...
...I generally trust the judgment of your Department H when it comes to these "super-people"...
...but you're now asking us to trust a national crisis to a man we know virtually nothing about.
Why is he holding out about his background, James?
He isn't, Admiral--at least, not voluntarily.
You see, Weapon X came to us with near-total amnesia--his memories wiped--
Let me guess--by persons unknown!
Gentlemen, we have already lost a crack commando team to this...this "incident"!
And now you want to send in a mental case who hasn't gone on a single mission yet?
I say we call in my second bomber squadron--turn that town into a crater before the situation gets any worse!
No! Civilian losses would be too high--
General, if I may...this is why the Department H super-agent program exists.
To do what conventional forces can't. To go where no one else can.
Can I have the next slide?
KA-KLIK
WOLVERINE
Let me show you how we would handle this situation with Weapon X.
Gentlemen, I give you...
Operation: Wolverine.

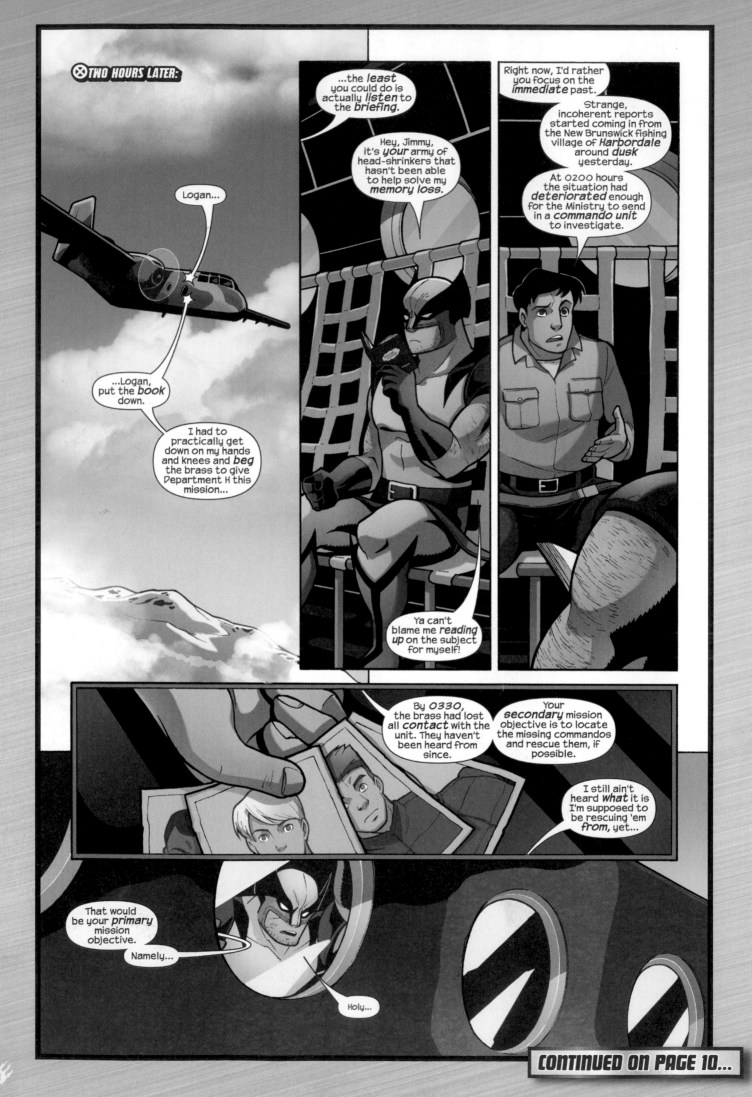

CONTINUED ON PAGE 10...

WOLVERINE

Ever wondered why Wolverine is the best at what he does? Read on to find out all about his many mutant talents!

WEAPON X

HEALING FACTOR!

Wolverine's main ability is his SuperHuman healing factor. This allows him to make speedy recoveries from severe injuries such as gunshot wounds, and be immune to almost all drugs and poisons!

ANIMAL INSTINCTS!

Wolvie has far superior senses to that of a normal human being. He can see and hear farther, and can recognise people from their scent alone! This allows him to track his prey with maximum efficiency!

SUPER STRATEGIST!

Wolverine has worked as a soldier, a samurai, a spy and a C.I.A. agent. His extensive experience on the battlefield and knowledge of operation procedures make him the perfect weapon for any mission!

FIGHTING SKILLS!

Wolverine has mastered virtually every martial art, including kung fu, ju-jitsu and street fighting! He has also had extensive training with various types of weapons and explosives!

LETHAL WEAPON!

Wolverine's entire skeleton has been fused with an indestructible metal called Adamantium, which has increased his strength and made his bones virtually unbreakable! He also has three retractable claws on each hand, which can cut through most materials!

CONTINUED FROM PAGE 8.

...find out what's *happened* to Harbordale...

...and how to *stop* it.

KINGDOM OF NO

WRITER FRED VAN LENTE ART GURIHIRU
LETTERS DAVE SHARPE COVER BY MCGUINNESS, FARMER AND PONSOR
PRODUCTION BY ANTHONY DIAL CONSULTING RALPH MACCHIO
EDITOR NATHAN COSBY EDITOR IN CHIEF JOE QUESADA
PUBLISHER DAN BUCKLEY EXECUTIVE PRODUCER ALAN FINE

No explanation can be ruled out at this point--the origin could even be *extra-terrestrial.*

Here's the *insertion* point.

Glad we had you train with the R.A.F. *paratroopers* for two weeks--

‡pffft‡ *Chutes* are for *sissies.*

Bring this tub right over the *treeline,* Flyboy!

You got it!

Logan...

Call me *"Wolverine!"* That's the new codename, right?

How can Department H get that big, fat *budget increase* you've been angling for if I don't show the top dogs what I can *do?*

And I aim to put on a *show.*

Please. The brass already thinks you're a dangerous *loose cannon.*

Don't do anything *stupid.*

Who...

...me?

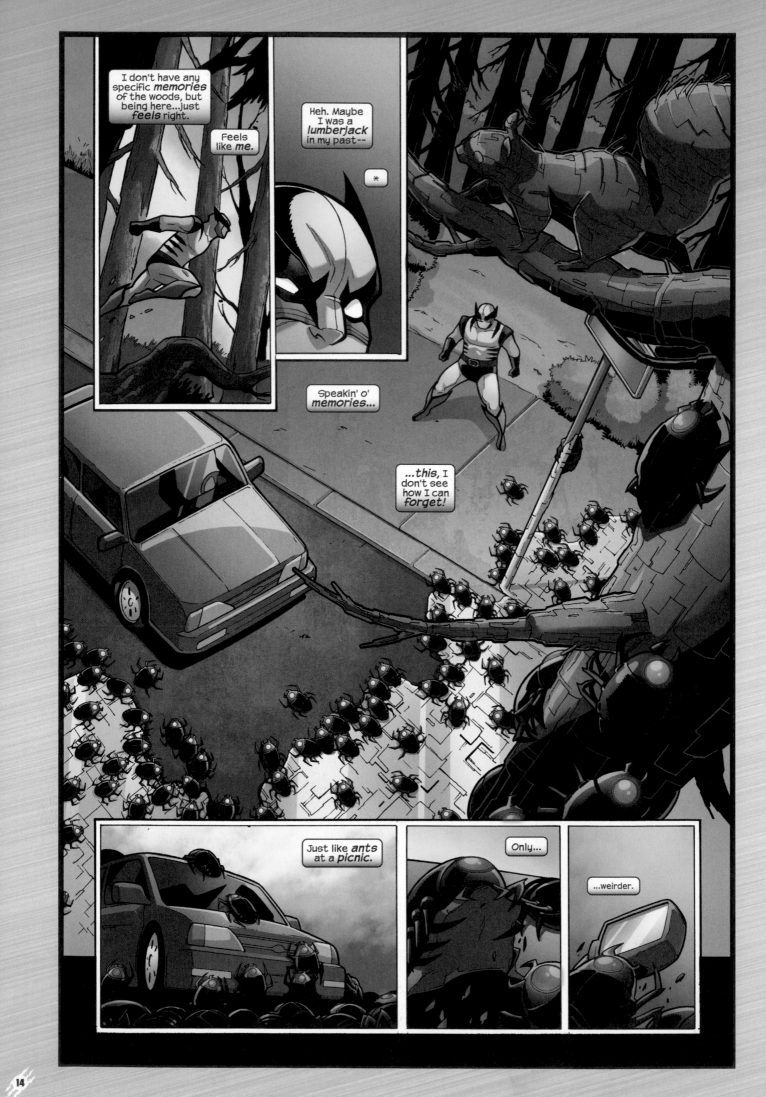

CONTINUED ON PAGE 19...

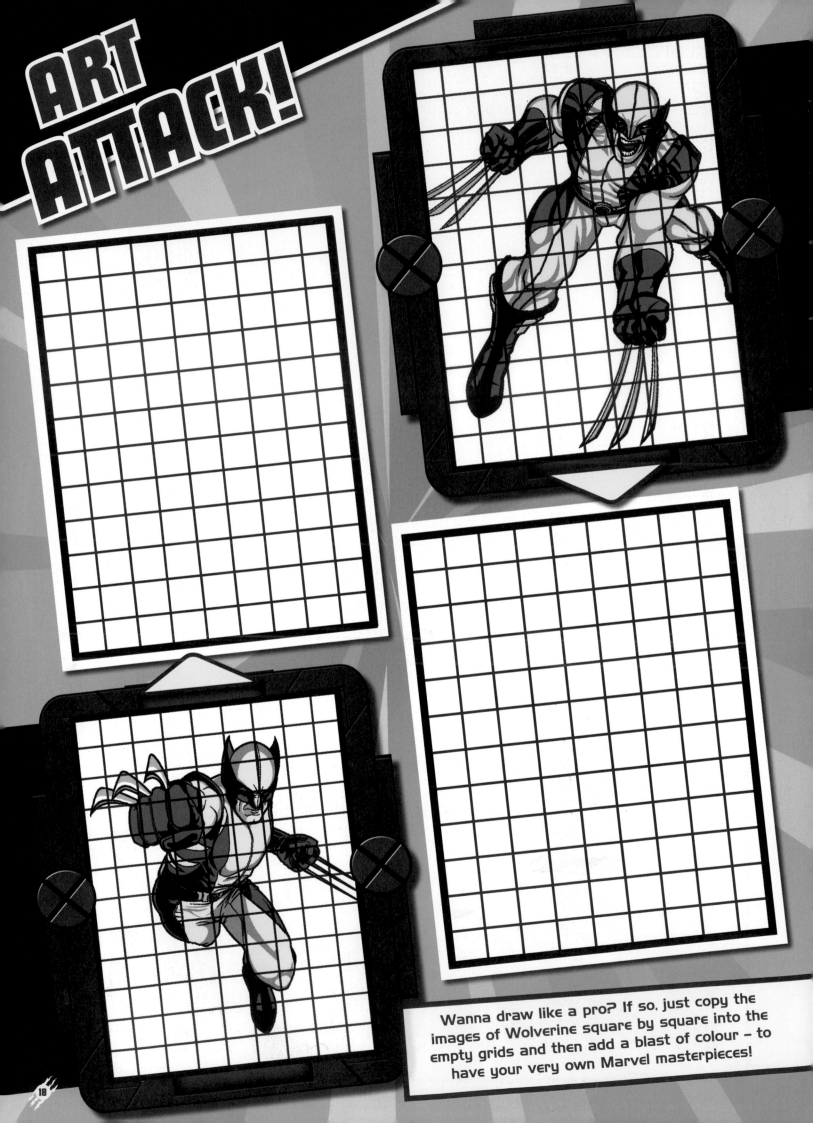

ART ATTACK!

Wanna draw like a pro? If so, just copy the images of Wolverine square by square into the empty grids and then add a blast of colour – to have your very own Marvel masterpieces!

CONTINUED ON PAGE 27...

STAY ON TRACK!

Can you lead Wolverine through the mysterious maze and avoid all the angry androids?

START

FINISH

TURN TO PAGE 62 FOR THE ANSWER!

CONTINUED FROM PAGE 25.

THE END!

THE ORIGINS OF... WOLVERINE

PART 2

DEPARTMENT H!

For many years Wolverine worked for the Canadian Government's Department H as a secret agent. Impressed with Wolverine's abilities, the Government planned to put together a team of super powered individuals who would protect the country from its enemies. This team was to be known as Alpha Flight.

ENTER, PROFESSOR X!

James Hudson hoped that Wolverine would one day lead the new team, but his plans were derailed by the arrival of Professor Charles Xavier. Professor X led a group of Super Heroes known as the X-Men – a team made up purely of mutants. He explained to Wolverine that he too was a mutant – a person born with a genetic quirk that gave them incredible super powers.

MASTER OF THE MIND!

In return for joining the X-Men the Professor told Wolverine that he could use his incredible psychic powers to help piece together the missing memories of his past. This was too good an offer for Wolverine to refuse and he resigned from his position to join the X-Men.

ESSENTIAL X-MAN!

More used to working on his own, Wolverine initially found it difficult being part of the X-Men. However he's learnt to adapt to being in a team and has since proved himself to be one of their most important members.

MUTANT MEMORIES!

Read on to discover some of Wolverine's most memorable moments as a member of the X-Men!

ALPHA FIGHT!

Shortly after joining the X-Men, Alpha Flight attacked the group, hoping to kidnap Wolverine and take him back to Canada to work for Department H. Big mistake!

MAGNETO'S REVENGE!

The X-Men's arch nemesis Magneto once used his magnetic powers to rip all of the adamantium out of Wolverine's body. Ouch!

DEATH BECOMES HIM!

For a short while, Wolverine was brainwashed by the evil mutant Apocalypse to become his most dangerous horseman – Death!

SCAREDY PANTS!

During a battle with the X-Men, Professor X's evil twin sister Cassandra Nova used her psychic powers to make Wolverine think he was a timid 7-year-old! He's doesn't like to be reminded about that one...

X-FORCE!

Wolverine is now the leader of his very own team of mutants – X-Force! This covert team of mutants are the best of the best and specialise in taking on the most deadly missions!

POWER PACK!

Granted amazing powers by a dying alien, Alex, Julie, Jack and Katie are four Super Hero siblings who use their incredible abilities to kick super villain butt! Read on to find out all about them!

LIGHTSPEED

Real Name: Julie Power
Abilities: Julie can fly at super sonic speeds of up to 600 mph. As she zooms through the air, she leaves a rainbow trail of light behind her.

ZERO-G

Real Name: Alex Power
Abilities: Alex has the power to control gravity. He can use this to make objects weightless. He can use his powers on his own body giving him the ability to fly.

ENERGIZER

Real Name: Katie Power
Abilities: Katie can disintegrate any form of matter and store the energy from the object in her body, expelling it later in the form of explosive energy bolts.

MASS MASTER

Real Name: Jack Power
Abilities: Jack can change his own density, allowing him to turn his body into an intangible cloud of gas.

The name's Wolverine.

They *say* I'm the *best there is* at *what I do.*

And *right now,* what I'm *doin'* seems *pretty darn weird.*

A FIGHT AT THE MUSEUM

Marc Sumerak--writer GuriHiru--art
Dave Sharpe--letters Irene Lee--production
Raplh Macchio--consulting Nathan Cosby--editor
Joe Quesada--editor in chief Dan Buckley--publisher

The *winged freak* calls himself *Sauron*.

He's as *nasty* as they *come*.

Flies, breathes fire, drains life energy, even *hypnotizes* people.

SLAMM!

He may *look* like a *dinosaur*, but he *ain't*. (Long story...)

Don't matter, though.

Either way he's about to *become* extinct...

Wait. That smell... Somethin' familiar. It *ain't* coming from lizard-lips here.

Smells like *candy*... and *gym* class...

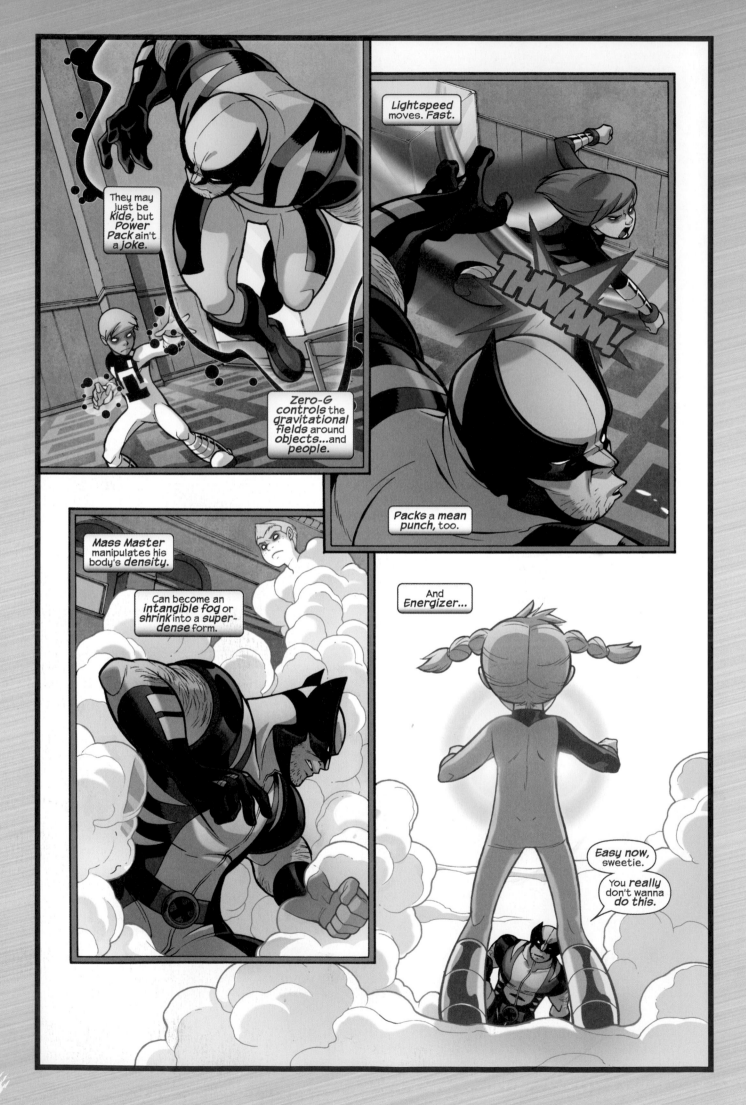

CONTINUED ON PAGE 41...

39

ART ATTACK!

COLOUR

GUIDE!

Wow! You wouldn't think it by reading the adventure story, but Wolvie really is friends with the Power Pack and this picture proves it! All you need to do is add the colour!

What if I were to *tell you* there was a *place in the world* where *dinosaurs* still roamed the earth *freely*?

I'd say you've been watching a *bit too much* Sci-Fi Channel.

As would *most of my* colleagues. But I *assure you* this place-- the Savage Land-- is *quite real.*

Come to *my lecture* and I'll--

No thanks, dude. I get *enough* lectures at home.

A shame.

If all goes as planned, you could've seen a *real live dinosaur!*

Count me in!

Count me out.

We'll *be there*, Dr.--?

Lykos. And you *won't regret it*, son.

I'm *sure* you'll find *everything* I have to *show you--*

--truly *fascinating...*

NEARBY...

I know, Cyke. I *said* I'd get there *soon* as I can.

You'd better. Your *students* at the *Xavier Institute* are depending on you, Logan.

Well, *you try* balancin' time as an *X-Man* and an *Avenger* with a *solo career!*

It *ain't easy!*

Then *maybe* it's time to reassess your *priorities?*

Hmmm... I *think* you *may* be right.

Help!

Some kind of *monster!*

Tell the *kids* that *class* is *cancelled* for today.

Somethin' *important* just came up.

Sorry, Cyke--break--up--can't--r--you!

But--

Logan! Wait!

Gotta go!

--a weird flying dinosaur thing!

That poor boy!

'Scuse me.

Comin' through.

I'm sorry, sir. We need you to leave.

We're having...umm... a pest control problem...

That's why I'm here, bub.

And you are...?

The exterminator.

Sauron?

And here I thought I was in for a challenge...

CONTINUED ON PAGE 52...

WOLVERINE &
POWER PACK'S PUZZLES

Hey, gang! Wolverine's teamed up with the Power Pack to bring you a couple of pages of near-impossible puzzles! Think you can complete them all? Let's find out...

THE RACE IS ON!

Wolverine, Lightspeed and Mass Master are having a race. See who finishes 1st, 2nd and 3rd by measuring each path with a piece of string!

FINISH!

TEAR UP!

Can you help piece together this damaged picture of Wolverine and Sauron going 12 rounds? Just write the number in the blank space where you think each piece goes...

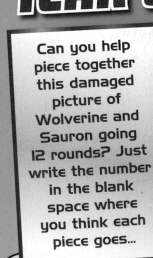

A.

B.

E.

D.

C.

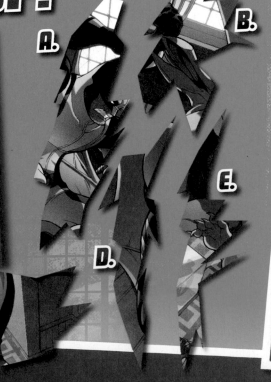

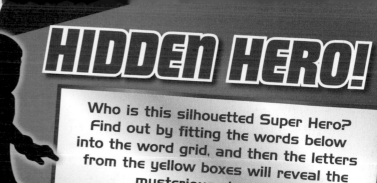

HIDDEN HERO!

Who is this silhouetted Super Hero? Find out by fitting the words below into the word grid, and then the letters from the yellow boxes will reveal the mysterious character!

SPEED

COURAGE

AGILITY   DAZZLING

STRENGTH

D a Z Z l i n g

S p e e D

S t r E n g t h

C o u r a G e

a g i l i t y

ANSWER:

PHOTO FAKERY!

Power Pack's favourite photo has been manipulated! Can you spot the 10 differences to the original?

ORIGINAL

TURN TO PAGE 62 FOR THE ANSWERS!

CONTINUED FROM PAGE 49.

HERO OR VILLAIN?

Take this quiz to see which hero, team, or villain you most resemble!

1. While walking along a street you notice a known criminal suspiciously running into a dark alleyway. Do you...

a) Call a friend and ask him to meet you near the alleyway?
b) Silently pursue the crook, using the shadows to stay unseen?
c) Chase after him and see what he's up to?

2. The criminal has teamed up with an unsavoury group of thugs all wearing balaclavas. Do you...

a) Call the cops – something is about to go down?
b) Stay hidden and wait for them to make their move?
c) Pull your balaclava from you pack pocket and slip it on?

3. The group run into a van parked outside a bank. Suddenly they jump out and storm into the bank! Do you...

a) Cover the front entrance while your friend covers the back exit – to make sure no one escapes?
b) Stealthily overpower one of the crooks and steal their disguise, so you can follow the rest undetected?
c) Run into the bank, but once inside, find out exactly how much money you are going to get for helping them?

4. The cops arrive and a big fight breaks out. Do you...

a) Join in and make sure no one escapes?
b) Go after the known criminal – he's the man behind the robbery?
c) Grab as much money as you can and escape out the nearest window?

MOSTLY A's
You like battling the bad guys with your friends beside you, just like the X-Men!

MOSTLY B's
You're fearless, an excellent hunter and like a rumble with the tough guys, just like Wolverine!

MOSTLY C's
You're worse than a common crook because you use them for your benefit, just like Magneto!

ART ATTACK!

COLOUR GUIDE!

When he's not tracking down super villains or fighting mad mutants with the X-Men, Wolverine's teaming up with the greatest group in the galaxy – the mighty Avengers! Bring this scene to life by assembling your pens and adding a blast of colour to Wolvie and his Super Hero friends!

WOLVIE'S TOP 10!

"When it comes to getting into fights, I'm an expert! In fact – I've scrapped with just about everyone one I've ever met! But here is my list of my top ten toughest fights!"

10.
Now I wouldn't say Elektra's the strongest I've ever faced, but it's still hard to fight an expert martial artist when she's as pretty as this!

9.
Spending as much time in the Canadian backcountry as I have, you get used to these not-so-friendly encounters with grizzly bears!

8.
Don't get me wrong, I normally like Spidey, but when the ol' web-head threw a snowball at me I didn't see the funny side!

7.
Agent Zero was on the same Weapons X program as me, so he knows how to fight! Worst still, he has the ability to absorb your attacks and use them against you!

6.
With expert fighting skills, a similar healing factor to mine, and enough weapons to take on a small country, Deadpool was a bit like fighting myself!

5.
This character is called Rapture. And when she gets angry she explodes with rage! Guess who made her angry...

3. Now I'm not in the habit of picking fights with one of the greatest heroes around, but occasionally Cap and I have had our disagreements... and when it happens, neither of us likes to back down!

4. This giant metal head is a Sentinel – designed to hunt and kill any mutant! But like I always say: the bigger they are, the harder they fall!

2. I've had more fights with this guy than hot dinners! Words can't describe how much I hate Sabretooth, but one thing I can say is he always gives as good as he gets!

1. What can I say about the Hulk? He's got a temper as bad as mine, but the only problem is when he gets angry, his strength increases! All I can say is it's a good job I have a superhuman healing factor...

ANSWERS!

Hey, bub, you better not be cheating! Make sure you complete the puzzles before looking at this page!

P26 STAY ON TRACK!

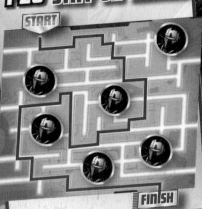

START

FINISH

P32 VILLAIN SEARCH!

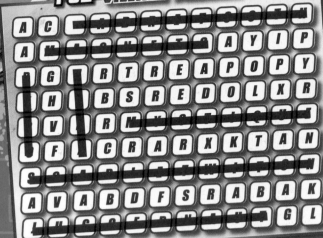

A	C										
A	L								A	Y	P
N	G	R	T	R	E	A	P	O	P	Y	
H	H	B	S	R	E	D	O	L	X	R	
V	V	R									
F	I	C	R	A	R	X	K	T	A	N	
A	V	A	B	D	F	S	R	A	B	A	K
										G	L

P32 MYSTERIOUS IMPOSTER!

P33 MENTAL MESSAGE!

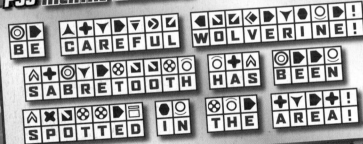

BE CAREFUL WOLVERINE!
SABRETOOTH HAS BEEN
SPOTTED IN THE AREA!

P33 SAVE STORM!

START

FINISH

P50 THE RACE IS ON!

1st   2nd   3rd

P51 HIDDEN HERO!

DAZZLING
SPEED
STRENGTH
COURAGE
AGILITY

ANSWER: ZEROG

P51 PHOTO FAKERY!

P50 TEAR UP!

A
D
B
E
C

Did you find all the 'X' logos? They were on pages 4,9,26,30,33,50,60 and 61!